Bringing Your Baby with Down Syndrome Home

A Guide to the First Month

Jeannie Visootsak, MD, FAAP
Deslie Quinby

ISBN-13: 978 0 692 30498 3
ISBN-10: 069 230 4983

This book was inspired by the desire to help new parents of a baby with Down syndrome during the most stressful and often overwhelming period of their parenthood—the first month of their baby's life.

Our book is born of a unique collaboration that fuses two vital perspectives: one from a medical doctor specializing in developmental-behavioral pediatrics, the other from a mother of a child with Down syndrome. Parents will find comfort in the mix of professional advice with the first-hand experiences and insight of a parent who was in their shoes just a few years back. Here we offer a step-by-step medical and intervention therapies checklist to address the common health, developmental, and social issues associated with Down syndrome, reminding parents of vital check-ups and testing, as well as words of wisdom from an empathetic parent to ease their fears.

Parents will embark on the first month of their baby's life armed with information and inspiration every day by drawing on this simple, practical resource that takes both the baby's and parents' well-being to heart.

Our book is a valuable resource for parents, Down syndrome parent support organizations, hospitals, and pediatrics, OB-GYN, and family practice offices.

TABLE OF CONTENTS

TABLE OF CONTENTS

ABOUT THE AUTHORS

Jeannie Visootsak, MD, FAAP, Associate Professor, is a board-certified Developmental-Behavioral Pediatrician at Emory University School of Medicine, Atlanta, GA. She is also the Medical Director of the Down Syndrome Clinic and Down Syndrome Clinical Trial Unit at Emory University. The Down Syndrome Clinic was established in 2003 to meet the needs of families and children with Down syndrome. Dr. Visootsak also serves on the Professional Advisory Council for the National Down Syndrome Congress and is an Advisory Board Member on the Down Syndrome Association of Atlanta.

Deslie Quinby was welcomed into the world of Down syndrome when her son JC was born with Down syndrome in 2004. Since then she has been an advocate and champion for her son and active in the Atlanta Down syndrome community. Deslie has her first Master's degree from the George Washington University and her second Master's from the Sloan School of Management at MIT. She is an accomplished businesswoman, having held executive positions at ChoicePoint, Carlson Wagonlit Travel, and The Weather Channel. She has also had experience running her own businesses. She is the mother of two boys: JC, age 10, and Skyler, age 9.

To all the children with Down syndrome and their parents who have shared their lives with me and continue to inspire me everyday
- Jeannie Visootsak, MD

To everyone who is reading this book for it is fear, wonderment or answers that are driving your need to read. It is with you in mind, that I share my personal experiences. I hope that you find peace within and hope that one day, I may meet your beautiful family and that you may meet mine.
- Deslie Quinby

Special thanks to Cheryl Strauss for her editorial assistance.

Day 1 Medical

Learning Your Baby May Have Down Syndrome

Congratulations on the arrival of your new baby! After months of pregnancy, your special day has come, bringing with it the most precious of gifts. The doctors and nurses who delivered and examined your newborn have noticed certain physical features that may indicate your baby has Down syndrome. From here, your doctor will order a chromosomal karyotype, a genetic map that shows all of your baby's chromosomes. This will allow the physicians to determine whether or not your baby has Down syndrome. Down syndrome is also known as trisomy 21, meaning your baby may have three copies of the 21st chromosome, instead of the usual two copies.

Although difficult, do your absolute best to remain positive as you await the genetic testing results. Devote all the energy you can to enjoying this special time with your newborn, focusing on the wonderful new life of your baby.

If you received a diagnosis during your pregnancy, you have already done plenty of reading about Down syndrome, and today is a special day for you and your baby as you meet each other for the first time.

> **Although difficult, do your absolute best to remain positive as you await the genetic testing results. Devote all the energy you can to enjoying this special time with your newborn, focusing on the wonderful new life of your baby.**

DAY 2 PARENT

While Anxiously Awaiting Your Test Results - Focus On Learning About Your Baby

You have just had a baby and learned that your baby may have Down syndrome. Who can guess what you are feeling? Perhaps a bit scared, a bit sad, a bit angry, and a bit unsure of your world. It's normal. You've just been thrown for a loop, and your coping mechanisms are in overdrive as you await the results of the karyotype.

If the tests show your child does not have Down syndrome, all your concern will have been for naught. You'll be greatly relieved and your world will continue along the lines you had expected. But since you are reading this book, it's likely that the test came back indicating your child does have Down syndrome. If that's the case: Welcome to our family—a family of people who have been gifted by a child who was born into a world a bit different. It's a beautiful world that you will get to experience and bring to others because of this special gift born to you and to your family alone.

It may not seem so now, and few will understand this if they have never received the news you have, but it is quite possible we are the lucky ones. I read something a few years after my son was born that I hold with me to this day: "You spend the first year of their life wondering how you will live with this little baby, and the rest of your years wondering how you will live without them." I have found this to be true.

All this is pretty deep stuff and probably sounds more like that old adage "every challenge makes you stronger," but that is not what's important right now. At the moment, you are merely waiting for a test result, the impact of which will affect you and your family, but not your newborn. You see, the baby isn't going to understand for many years that they have Down syndrome or that they are different. The fact is, all your newborn needs is what every other newborn needs: to be fed, to be changed, to be held, and to be loved.

Our best advice at this juncture is to live for the moment. Focus on what the baby needs: warmth and love. Most children born with Down syndrome are relatively easy babies. They don't cry much or demand attention; you will need to proactively provide for them. In fact, it's easy to get bogged down trying to learn about the baby's potential diagnosis and its implications for your family, inadvertently, while the baby is quietly alone in her bassinet. Don't let this happen. Be selfish and lose yourself in those innocent infant moments.

Day 3 Medical

While Anxiously Awaiting Your Test Results, Enlist Support From Others

As the days pass, they may be split between smiles and concerns. This is absolutely normal as you continue to await the findings of the chromosome study. Remain strong and confident that, whatever the test results show, you will still be holding a beautiful gift, swaddled in your arms. Your baby needs your warmth and confidence. Remember that your good health, physical and emotional, is important for you and your new little one.

If you are feeling very concerned and stressed out—and this is completely normal—take full advantage of the support of family and friends. Whether you have a large group or a small group to rely on, seek out their encouragement. Keep in mind that the quantity of social support is not as important as the quality. Share your emotions with your brothers, sisters, parents, grandparents, friends, nurses, and physicians. Allow them to offer you company and reassurance.

Whether your baby does indeed have Down syndrome or not, a birth is a wonderful change. With any change comes some degree of anxiety and possibly stress. You are strong, but will be even stronger with a loving support system behind you.

DAY 4 PARENT

Naming Your Baby

Before leaving the hospital, it is best to name your baby so the hospital can put the baby's name on the birth certificate, saving you lots of effort later. You may already have a name picked out. We did. We had chosen a family name, John Conrad; John after my father, and Conrad after my mother-in-law. I had heard that the use of family names helps to make a child feel connected. I don't know if that's true or not, but I liked the idea, and we both liked the name, John Conrad.

But, we thought, our baby might have Down syndrome. How would our family members feel having him named after them? Perhaps I should save this name for our second child and give this unique child a unique name? Back and forth, my overactive brain would go. What were we going to name our little man?

Finally, holding back tears and pretending it was no big deal, I separately asked my mother-in-law and my father what they thought of the name John Conrad. They were honored, their faces lighting up with pride. This would not be the first time I would imagine an issue that just wasn't there. I still feel silly for having the concern, but in some way asking and seeing their pride comforted me. Our little guy had already won the hearts of my family, as he already had mine.

After I got over this emotional naming hurdle, my husband and I began to think more practically. We wanted to give our son a name that would be relatively easy for him to say and to spell. John was short and pretty easy, but John Conrad is a bit of a mouthful. In the hospital, with great foresight that sometimes comes when you need it most, we made the decision that our John Conrad would be JC. Notice how easy it is to write and say the name JC. As hoped, our little guy was able to speak his name early on and was amongst the first in his class to write his name.

Much later, when JC was in Pre-K, we were out and about and someone asked him his name. He looked at them proudly and said: "My name is John Conrad." We had always called him JC. I didn't even know he knew his entire name, never mind being able to relay it unprompted to a third party. My point is that no matter what name you pick, your child is going to know it, and most likely be able to say it and spell it, too.

Day 5 Medical

Recognizing Down Syndrome After Birth

After labor and delivery, health professionals at the hospital may suspect your newborn has Down syndrome based on what they observe in terms of physical features and low muscle tone. Facial features characteristic of Down syndrome can be quite variable, but often include slanting eyes, epicanthal folds (small folds of skin at the inside corners of the eyes), a small nose, a tongue that protrudes, and small ears. Some babies will have an extra fold of skin on the back of their neck and a single transverse crease across one or both palms. Every child is different, so you may not see all or any of these features. This is your baby, and he or she will look like you and your family!

Day 6 Parent

The Most Beautiful Baby In The World

If you read the many books on Down syndrome, you'll find that they discuss all the physical markings that help the medical community identify a child who may have been born with Down syndrome. This can be a bit frightening. My child has epicanthal folds, a transverse crease, smallish features, making the tongue appear oversized and hard to fit the mouth, and the list goes on. It's now that you need to step back and take a moment to really look at your baby. You'll see that these markers and your gene pool have created a Picasso. Babies with Down syndrome are really beautiful and much sought after for photographs, calendars, and magazines. Unbeknownst to me, JC and I were at Disability Day, and we ended up on the cover of "Making a Difference" magazine the next month. When your newborn is ready to face the world, make sure to walk tall and proud. Your child will be cooed over.

DAY 7 MEDICAL

The Echocardiogram

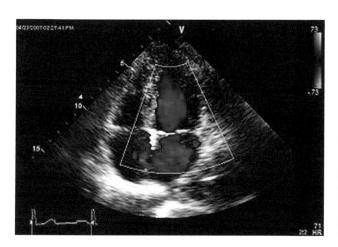

As much love as there is in your baby's heart, he or she may have difficulties with that special organ. About half of all babies with Down syndrome encounter one or even a few cardiac issues. Because this is widely understood by medical professionals, your baby will have an echocardiogram (ECHO), one of the most common tests used to diagnose heart issues, scheduled shortly after birth. All newborns with Down syndrome will have an ECHO performed before they are discharged from the hospital. Remember the ultrasound of your baby while in the womb? The OB/GYN or nurse placed cool globs of gel on the pregnant belly and used a special wand to pick up and send out sound waves, or echoes. The sound waves were processed by the ultrasound machine to display an image of your baby. The echocardiogram is essentially an ultrasound, but this time one that zeroes in on your baby's heart. A child with Down syndrome may be born with a congenital heart defect. Congenital means the heart defect is present at birth. Some of these abnormalities can resolve themselves over time, while others may require surgery. The cardiologist will decide what, if any, steps should be taken once he or she conducts the ECHO.

Day 8 Parent

Understanding The Precautions

Congratulations! You got through your first week and through many medical tests, most of which are nerve-wracking for you, but painless for the baby. You may have been moved to a private room in a part of the hospital for high-risk patients. You've probably been met with a quiet kindness and intense concern that unfortunately doesn't come with many answers. At least, this was our experience. We found, however, that almost everything that was done was done out of caution more than need. Our baby was fine. Remember: even though Down syndrome is a more common disability, it is still fairly rare, and most people (doctors too) are not used to dealing with it regularly. When something is different, it's human nature to want to be cautious. Just as Down syndrome is new to you, it's most likely out of the routine for others, too.

You will find that some people don't know how to act, and because you are in a hospital where they could be held responsible for anything that goes wrong, they are extra cautious. Hospital personnel go into "we're going to play it safe" mode. Safe in what they do and safe in what they say. Unfortunately, due to the litigious nature of our society, they have reason to be careful in terms of their behavior.

What this means to you is that everyone is on their "best" behavior, which can be a bit overwhelming. You get a lot of quiet attention. Although it may seem a bit awkward, the extra attention and care, even if it is somewhat understated in its delivery, is probably a good thing. Better safe than sorry, as the old saying goes. My advice is to get people talking about other things: the weather, where they are from. This will relax them, and while it won't make the elephant in the room go away, it will put a semblance of normalcy on the situation.

Day 9 Medical

Early Intervention

Your child will be referred to the state's Early Intervention Program shortly after birth to ensure that you have help to maximize his or her potential. Early Intervention is a plan of active commitment to the wellbeing of infants and toddlers with special needs that focuses on gathering beneficial interventional resources as soon as possible. Adopting an early-intervention mindset is key to ensuring that your baby develops as successfully as possible. The diagnosis of Down syndrome most certainly does not imply a lack of development. Just like a typical baby, a baby with Down syndrome is expected to progress functionally in all areas of development, including gross motor, fine motor, language, and social. The rate at which your baby acquires some of these skills will vary from a typical child, but with some honest and loving effort, you child will continue to make progress. In any case, remember that your baby will follow a positive trajectory when it comes to these milestones, if you first believe that he or she can, and second, if you choose to work closely with the guidance of interventional therapists. It will be of great reassurance and relief for you to know that, as part of the Early Intervention plan, there is a wealth of community support in the form therapies from birth to age 3 (physical, occupational, and speech, among others) for babies with Down syndrome.

DAY 10: PARENT

The Visit

As part of this mostly quiet support in the hospital, you may also receive what I deemed "The Visit." I remember it vividly. It's the visit where they tell you that you can give your baby away. I don't know if it's standard procedure for a Down syndrome diagnosis, but I do know that a similar option was not offered when my second child was born without Down syndrome.

Was this done for liability purposes? Was this offered because many parents choose this option? Is the hospital trying to protect an innocent child from unfit parents? Sad questions with potentially sadder answers. For me, as a new mom, the question did not feel good.

I was not prepared for a woman I didn't know to come into my room and talk about the "many people who want to adopt a child with Down syndrome." I did not want to hear about the "…wait list for adoption for children with Down syndrome." Or how I had the "…. ability to put my child up for adoption, where they would be given the support they needed." I knew what my baby needed. My baby needed me.

Wow, my baby needed me! I didn't even know I had motherly instincts (this was our first child) until now, when they kicked into overdrive—medicated overdrive, I might add. I wanted this woman away from my baby and me immediately. I often wonder if others, who may be financially or emotionally unequipped to handle the news at the moment, make rash decisions they later come to regret. Most of the families we know (regardless of income) do really well including a child with Down syndrome into their families. Here's a little known fact:

"There are fewer divorces in families who have kids with Down syndrome."

I believe it's because these children bring love with them everywhere, and it spreads like wildfire. So, if you do get a visit, really think through the implications of the easy-out being offered.

DAY 11: MEDICAL

Hypotonia

Hypotonia means, "low muscle tone," and it is commonly present in nearly all newborns with Down syndrome. Your baby's low muscle tone may influence the way you hold your baby—be sure to provide plenty of head support during this time, so there is no head lag or floppiness. With ongoing physical therapy, your baby's tone will improve as he progresses through the typical sequence of rolling over, sitting, crawling, and eventually walking appropriately. Patricia Winders, a physical therapist who has extensive experience in working with children with Down syndrome, has published the book "Gross Motor Skills in Children with Down Syndrome." She suggests that the appropriate goal of physical therapy for children with Down syndrome is not to accelerate their rate of gross motor development; rather, the goal of physical therapy is to minimize the development of abnormal compensatory movement patterns that children with Down syndrome are prone to develop. In addition, since gross motor development is the first learning task the child experiences, it provides parents with the first opportunity to explore how their child learns. For these reasons, it is important that you contact your state's Early Intervention Program to initiate a physical therapy evaluation and ongoing therapy for your child.

...the appropriate goal of physical therapy for children with Down syndrome is not to accelerate their rate of gross motor development; rather, the goal of physical therapy is to minimize the development of abnormal compensatory movement patterns that children with Down syndrome are prone to develop.

DAY 12: PARENT

Down Syndrome - The Few Things You Need To Do

It seems like life is coming at you fast, but you actually have tons of time to learn and become familiar with Down syndrome. Babies with Down syndrome develop at a different rate, allowing you more time to get your mind around everything you need to know. So, when you finally have some quiet time, don't feel pressured into having to do more Down syndrome research; take some time for yourself, instead.

If you're a new mom, you've just been through an ordeal both physically and emotionally. Take care of yourself and give yourself the breaks you need. The Down syndrome information is important, but it will be there when you do have time. Ironically, it is only after you digest the information that you begin to understand there isn't much to do at this point that is any different from what you would do for a typical developing baby.

To save you some time, the few things that begin to be important early on (within the first three months) are the following:

1) Get in touch with your Early Intervention organization. They can tell you what resources are available and give you some references for physical therapists.

2) Understand what aid is available for you to help support your child. Your early intervention organization should have lots of information on this.

3) Understand what support groups are available to you, your child, and your family.

4) Start looking for a physical therapist to help your child with early physical milestones: turning her head, rolling, and sitting.

Another short cut for you is to talk to another parent who has a young child with Down syndrome. They have recently been through everything you are dealing with and will have many answers for you, including answers to the questions above.

For now, that's about it. Of course, as with any child, if there are medical considerations beyond the Down syndrome, the medical issues become the top priority.

DAY 13: MEDICAL

The Search For A Pediatrician

Regardless of what your child's needs may be, seeking out a pediatrician receptive to those specific needs is truly important. Every pediatrician attended medical school, and each one completed pediatrics residency training. So what sets them apart from one another? What qualities should a parent look for? Surely all parents hope to find themselves in the company of a competent and personable doctor, and those characteristics will absolutely have a positive impact on your child's pediatric visits; however, the most important trait to look for during your search among general pediatricians is a willingness to not only listen to your very specific issues related to Down syndrome, but also to learn. While general pediatricians are a wealth of knowledge and a great resource, their expertise may not be specific to Down syndrome. Good pediatricians, like any good doctor, are open to a better understanding of the specifics of their patients, and may refer your child to specialists when necessary. It is important to ask questions and discuss any medical concerns with your child's pediatrician. Your child's pediatrician may also refer you to a Down syndrome clinic in your area so your child can be closely monitored by specialists and/or therapists with special interest and expertise in Down syndrome.

There are several health issues that occur occasionally in children with Down syndrome. The pediatrician will follow the health supervision guidelines for managing the care of children with Down syndrome to monitor hearing, vision, thyroid, sleep, feeding, etc...

The pediatrician may refer your child to your state's early intervention program. Your child will be assigned a case coordinator who will conduct an initial assessment. This evaluation is used to determine the status of his or her developmental skills. It is essentially a stepping-stone to gain relevant insight and therapies for your child's specific developmental needs. From this point, your case coordinator will create your child's very own therapy plan, aptly deemed the "Individualized Family Service Plan," or IFSP. Notice the inclusion of family—your baby, family and friends, pediatrician, and your newly recruited early intervention therapists together form a team, all on your side! This plan provides therapeutic activities and practical strategies that families can use to promote their child's development throughout the day, every day. Therapists — physical therapists and speech therapists, among others — will be assigned to work with your child and provide productive in-home activity programs for you, as parents. Early intervention can make a lifetime of difference!

Day 14 Parent

Communications With Friends And Family

One of the things my husband dealt with quite soon after the birth of our son was communications with our friends and family. I had an emergency C-section and was on a morphine drip for the first few days, so most of our communication was left to him. Luckily, my husband does a lot of communications professionally. I give him tons of credit for the way he handled sharing our information and keeping our friends and family in the loop, enabling them to support us in the ways we needed.

We actually didn't mention that our son was being tested for Down syndrome in our first email; we didn't want to alarm or concern people until we knew for sure that he had it. In retrospect, I think this was probably the right thing to do. It gave JC a more typical entrance into our world. Also, since everyone knew JC and I were both healthy (via photos and email), when they learned JC had Down syndrome a few days later, it made the news a bit less scary.

Below you'll find a set of sample communications, both with and without the mention of Down syndrome. You might like to adapt them for your use, sending different e-mails to people depending on how close they are to you.

1.) Sample E-mail: No mention of Down syndrome

Deslie and Douglas would like to introduce their son, John Conrad ("J.C."). He was born on Thursday, January 29th 2004, at 2:23 pm. JC came in at six pounds, nine ounces, and his favorite pastimes include eating, sleeping, and just kind of lying there with his eyes open. JC and Mom returned home from the hospital on Monday, and both are doing great! – Photos Attached

2.) Sample E-mail for those you want to give a heads up to about the possibility of Down syndrome

Deslie and Douglas would like to introduce you to their son, John Conrad ("J.C."). He was born on Thursday, January 29th 2004, at 2:23 pm. JC came in at six pounds, nine ounces, and his favorite pastimes include eating, sleeping, and just kind of lying there with his eyes open. Though he and mom are doing well, we did want share that we've learned there is a possibility that he has Down syndrome. They are running tests now. As we learn more, we will keep you posted. – Photos Attached.

3.) Sample E-mail: After Down syndrome is confirmed

We have just learned our son, John Conrad, was born with Down syndrome. We don't know too much about Down syndrome at this point, but we do know that our son is healthy and that people with Down syndrome can live long and fulfilling lives. Down syndrome is a fairly common chromosome disorder caused by the presence of an extra chromosome number 21 (it is sometimes referred to as trisomy 21). The presence of the extra chromosome affects each child differently. How different and in which ways, we will learn as he grows. We've shared below some resources that the doctors have given us for you to review along with us if you are interested. This is all happening quite fast and unexpectedly, so we greatly appreciate your support.

Day 15: Medical

A Pioneer And Someone To Thank

Where did the name Down syndrome come from? In 1866, Dr. John Langdon Down described a group of patients who looked and acted very much alike, despite no familial relation. It was a puzzle to him: Why did these patients have so much in common? He revealed that they had language problems and simultaneously exhibited sociability and humor. These "charming" patients were also described as having physical features unlike those of other children with known intellectual disabilities.

"Down syndrome" was coined to recognize Dr. John Langdon Down's immense contribution to the diagnosis and better understanding of Down syndrome. His investigations have since helped countless children and families, as Down

syndrome turns out to be quite common. In fact, according to current statistics, it is present in approximately 1 in every 691 births, approximately 6000 births per year in the US. It is present in all ethnic groups, socioeconomic levels, and geographic regions. As you can see, you are not alone.

DAY 16: PARENT

Breast-Feeding

As a first-time mom, I had done lots of reading and had my heart set on breast-feeding my child. I tried in the hospital with the support of a lactation specialist and many nurses, but JC was having trouble suckling. Babies with Down syndrome have low muscle tone, which can make nursing an extremely arduous task. But, I was not deterred; I pumped and pumped and pumped. I'd take a break and try to get JC to feed, and then I'd pump some more. I did this for six weeks with little success. JC's muscles were still not strong enough for him to adequately latch on to my breast. Ultimately, since I was due back to work, I made the decision to move to bottle-feeding with formula.

I was able to breast-feed my second son. I loved it and wish that I had persevered when trying to breast-feed JC. In hindsight, I would have pumped for many more months. I miss not having had that experience with him and feel I robbed both him and me of something very special. I have a friend who pumped for a year while waiting for her daughter, also born with Down syndrome, to be able to breast-feed. At the time, I thought she was nuts. Now, I wish that I had been as determined. I have the utmost respect for the very precious gift she gave to her daughter and to herself.

Even though, looking back I say that I would have pumped till JC was ready, I am cognizant that in all honesty I may not have done it. Most likely if I had, I would not have gotten pregnant with my second son. My point here is to make the best decision you can for you given your circumstances and don't beat yourself up over it.

Day 17: Medical

Dr. Len Leshin's Website

Dr. Len Leshin can wholeheartedly relate to parents of a child with Down syndrome, as he is such a parent himself. His son Avi has Down syndrome and has inspired him to write articles, as father and physician, for the benefit of parents newly in his shoes. In addition to publishing the list of Down syndrome clinic resources, Dr. Leshin has also published more extensive information on various medical aspects of Down syndrome, covering topics that we will delve into later, but that you can explore further at any time.

On his website, http://ds-health.com, Dr. Leshin offers his own writings on health issues typically associated with Down syndrome (such as cardiac and gastrointestinal problems and sleep issues) and general pediatric information, as well. He also includes articles from other contributors in the field of physical therapy, speech therapy, etc. We recognize how busy new parents are, so once you find yourself with time to read more, BABIES with Down Syndrome, A New Parent's Guide, edited by Susan Skallerup, is thorough and information-packed, offering details necessary to answer more complicated questions as they arise over time.

Day 18: Parent

Coming Home — A Time For Tears

I had a C-Section and was on morphine during my stay at the hospital. Down syndrome had not yet been confirmed, though we knew it was likely based on the nurses' actions and the baby's demeanor. We received our diagnosis when I was at home with family, and with no more painkillers flowing through my system. I now knew for sure that my son was going to be disabled; yet, I had no experience to draw upon. I had never been around anyone with a significant disability. I had always shied away from things like disabilities that involved emotional pain.

So, it was in the quiet of my home, surrounded by family that I shed my first tear. I was sad, and I was scared. Not only was I losing the child that I had imagined I would have, I also feared for my son. I imagined him being alienated, having no friends, being teased and not understanding that he was being teased. I imagined him being the kid who was made to eat worms, dunked in toilets; the one whose lunch money was stolen daily. I imagined him growing up alone and isolated: no girlfriends, no college, no wife, no children, and worst of all totally dependent. This was not the life I had imagined for my child. Nor the life I wanted for my child. My heart broke.

As you can see, I was pretty unprepared for my future. My turning point as I distinctly remember it came one day when I was attempting to breast-feed my son. The breast-feeding was going horribly. I couldn't get him to latch on to my breast long enough to feed. I was sitting in our rocking chair with JC clasped to me, with streams of tears falling down on my son. I wondered how this would impact him and if he could sense how distraught I was. The thought sickened me, and I struggled to contain my grief. I would not cry again when holding him, because you see, I already loved him to pieces. I was already becoming the person that I needed to be. Yet, at that moment, I was distraught. Looking back, I think I needed to go through the pain of loss in order to move forward. It would not take long for me to realize that my fears were mostly unwarranted. My son is accepted. In fact, in many instances, people fall all over themselves to support and accept us.

JC has been in an inclusive classroom setting since kindergarten. He is accepted unconditionally. He's not bullied. He's loved and brings love and compassion into his classroom, because he's so wonderfully extroverted and caring. He plays on many sports teams; both with typical children and with other children with special needs. His future is bright. He can get married, go to college, get a job, and if I do my job right, he will be pretty independent. He will lead a rich life. He will make a difference in our world; when someone has this much love to offer, it's impossible not too.

DAY 19: MEDICAL

An Inspiring Story For Your Spare Time

Jennifer Graf Groneberg is Avery's mother. She has authored the book "Road Map to Holland: How I Found My Way Through My Son's First Two Years with Down Syndrome". She describes her experience of raising a child with Down syndrome as "like planning a trip to Italy only to get off the plane and discover you're actually in Holland." As Jennifer explains, in this unexpected situation: "You need a new road map, and fast…." Learning your newborn has Down syndrome requires this "new road map," the information and support to ensure that your child reaches his or her full potential, which is the destination, of sorts.

Jennifer's son, Avery, was diagnosed with Down syndrome shortly after birth, and she shares her journey of coming to terms with the diagnosis and developing new and supportive relationships. She tells a beautiful story about the relationship between a mother and her son, "the child she didn't know she wanted, the child she always needed." The book is a valuable resource and companion for new parents.

Day 20: Parent

Coming Home — The Crying Continues

So, I was grieving for my son, his future, and the baby I didn't have, but that wasn't enough. I now had a new set of concerns to face. What type and how much care would he need? How would we provide his care? Would we be able to afford it? Would we go broke providing for his needs? How would we decide between his needs versus expense? Would these decisions drive our family apart? How would I learn how to raise this child? How would we work his care into our already busy lives? I shed many tears over each of these questions, only later to find out that most of the concerns were for naught.

JC does require some special care, mostly therapies and annual checkups by specialists. Fortunately, due to his diagnosis of Down syndrome, he qualifies for Medicaid. If you choose doctors who take Medicaid, this will reduce your single greatest cost burden. It is always my first question when choosing doctors. Besides medical concerns, we also needed an adequate child-care facility, since both my husband and I worked full time. Although we found a local church day care that welcomed him, they didn't have a spot for a few months. In the interim, a neighbor's daughter who was home on summer break from college came to our house and watched over him during the early days. Everything had fallen into place. All was well. We were going to be able to do this.

Then JC got very sick from being exposed to normal day care viruses. His pediatrician recommended he be removed from the day care setting. So much for well-laid plans! We were now in the market for a nanny. Again, things somehow just seemed to work. We not only found a nanny, we found an incredible nanny who had experience working with children with special needs. I knew she would be our nanny when we interviewed her. She was the only one of five who, after seeing JC in his bouncy hooked up to little oxygen tubes and a great big oxygen tank (he was recovering from RSV, baby pneumonia that any child is prone to), engaged with him naturally. She got down on her hands and knees and asked, "Can I hold him?" I was hooked; she was hired. To this day, Ms. Pat continues to be part of our family.

While JC's care is different in some ways, I wouldn't say that it's harder than our care for our other son. It is simply different, and since it's different, there aren't many resources to rely on. This means we sometimes have to do a bit more digging and networking to feel good about the decisions we make. Still, neither his care nor the expenses associated with it have become the burden I had feared.

DAY 21: MEDICAL

Down Syndrome Clinics

Whether you have been referred by a pediatrician or have decided to take it upon yourself to bring your baby to a specialist, you will be comforted to know that there are specialists with expertise in Down syndrome all over the United States who are ready to address particular issues that arise over time and to offer medical and developmental evaluations and resources to ensure your new baby continues to make progress towards her full potential. Your child will typically be evaluated by a developmental-behavioral pediatrician during a visit at the Down Syndrome Clinic. A developmental-behavioral pediatrician has expertise to comprehensively assess your child's development and address medical issues that may influence your child's development, learning and behavior. A developmental -behavioral pediatrician will be a great resource for you and your baby, ensuring that he is making progress in all areas of development: gross motor, fine motor, language, and social. These specialists do not replace the care your child receives from the general pediatrician, but they are an additional resource. We encourage you to make an appointment at a Down syndrome clinic as soon as possible—the sooner, the better!

A list of Down syndrome clinics in the USA is located at

www.ndsccenter.org/resources/healthcare/medical-clinic-listing

DAY 22: PARENT

You Are A Special Mom

As far as being accepted and included, I mentioned earlier that many people have gone out of their way to make us feel wanted. What effect does this have? Well, instead of being ostracized and feeling alienated, I feel special. People will often say "your son is so special," or he has "special needs," but in actuality, I am the one who feels special, like I'm a very special mom.

I've heard stories about children choosing their parents. When I have a quiet moment to myself, I like to think that my sons chose me as their mom. That they knew I would accept them for who they are and not try to make them into something different, that I would protect them, cherish them, teach them, advocate for them and become the person they need me to be. You too will become the mom that your child needs; just by reading this book, you have already taken a step in that direction.

DAY 23: MEDICAL

Down Syndrome Explained

Your baby is now three weeks old and enjoying the new and different world outside of mom's womb, soaking up the first glimpses of light and smiling faces. Three weeks also means you may have received the definitive results from your child's chromosome study. If you haven't yet, you will very soon. As you know, a chromosomal karyotype for Down syndrome will typically show three copies of chromosome 21 (95% of Down syndrome cases have this type, known as standard trisomy 21). But there are actually three different types of Down syndrome: standard trisomy 21, mosaicism, and translocation.

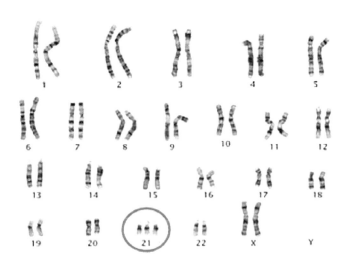

Mosaicism is the rarest version of Down syndrome. Like mosaic art on a tabletop or picture frame with many tiles of different colors, perhaps some blue and some red, a child with mosaicism has some cells with the third copy of chromosome 21 and other cells without the extra copy. The ratio of trisomy cells to non-trisomy cells can vary. Finally, in translocation, a portion of chromosome 21 breaks off and attaches to another chromosome. This means that the baby does not have an entire extra copy of chromosome 21, but has a chromosome with extra genetic material from chromosome 21.

Ask your doctor about speaking with a geneticist or genetic counselor, who will offer you a very detailed explanation of Down syndrome and what it means for your baby as he or she grows up.

DAY 24: PARENT

Silent Victim Or Superhero?

Sometime, either during or after the tears, you realize you have a decision to make. Are you a victim or a superhero, or somewhere in the middle of that continuum? I tend to come down on the side of superhero. You have a choice to make either consciously or subconsciously. Who are you going to become for this baby? I actually believe (and it's taken me awhile to come to grips with this fact) that being a mom changes you a lot. Your identity, as you know it, morphs into a new identity: Who are you now? What are you going to give up? What are you going to gain? What is this new identity like? Are you going to be the frazzled mom who barely makes it through the are you going to roll up your sleeves and learn what this new world is all about?

I think this change probably happens to all moms, whether or not they have a child with special needs. It's just that when special needs are involved, you need to face this fact sooner.

DAY 25: MEDICAL

What Are Gross Motor Skills?

Gross motor skills are those that incorporate your "big" muscles—those needed for reaching milestones such as rolling over, sitting, crawling, walking, and running. As we touched on earlier, the rate of gross motor development in a child with Down syndrome may be impacted by several factors, including hypotonia, ligamentous laxity (loose ligaments causing increased joint mobility), decreased strength, and shorter arms and legs. However, these problems will not prevent your child from achieving her motor milestones! Because we recognize these factors as potential barriers, it is important to begin physical therapy shortly after your baby is home. If you do not address the hypotonia, ligamentous laxity, decreased strength, etc., early on, your child can develop compensatory movement patterns. For example, your child may scoot instead of crawl, because of decreased strength and because scooting still gets the job done. The appropriate patterns of development in gross motor skills include the following sequence: rolling over, sitting, crawling, and then finally walking!

Day 26: Parent

Mini-Me Syndrome

I've read that in many instances new parents unknowingly feel their child is a direct extension of themselves. You have all heard the saying "a chip off the old block." With a typical developing child, parents are able to hold onto this delusion for a long time (sometimes forever). Mostly, however, parents realize somewhere between childhood and puberty that their child is uniquely their own person, with their own likes and dislikes and the ability to make their own good (and bad!) decisions. When you have a child with a disability, you understand that they are uniquely their own person from day one. In some ways, I think this is a blessing. The child grows up being who they are supposed to be, rather than what you expect them to be.

> **Laughing together and crying together, sharing emotional stories and simple tips, you will find great comfort and relief in these rewarding connections.**

Day 27: Medical

"It Takes A Village"

Every state offers support groups for families of children with Down syndrome. It may seem an obvious suggestion, but the value of a social network of understanding peers simply cannot be overstated. Sharing your story with people like yourself, people who deal with the issues you deal with, who encounter the good times and the more difficult times that you do, is essential for your wellbeing as a parent and as a person. Laughing together and crying together, sharing emotional stories and simple tips, you will find great comfort and relief in these rewarding connections. Connecting with other parents will also afford your child his or her own links to potentially lifelong friends and playmates. Here we spend a great deal of time discussing your baby and your life in medical terms, but physicians understand as well as anyone that social and emotional health is intimately intertwined with physical wellbeing and is without doubt essential, so take advantage of Down syndrome family support groups in your community; reach out to others and allow them to reach out to you.

DAY 28: PARENT

Family Support

At the time JC was born and shortly thereafter, I was so concerned about the baby and myself that I didn't spend much time thinking about how everyone else was doing. I didn't shut myself off from people, though. I let them support our family, and in some ways I think having them support us was therapeutic for them. They became involved in our care and our lives and quickly fell in love with our little man. Love is a wondrously powerful thing. Once in love, you realize everything is going to be OK. It's going to be OK because you're going to make sure it's OK! That is how it's been for us; my entire family accepting JC and laying the ground work for him to be included in our family, our community, our schools, and life itself.

My mom and dad bought a house in Georgia. They now live here about a month every quarter. My in-laws moved here permanently from New York. I don't know that everyone's family would be able to make such drastic life changes and, in all honesty, I'm not sure that it is needed, either. But, I also think most families want to be there to support you; you just have to help them figure out how. Sometimes a phone call or smile is all you need. Other days you might want help writing letters to congressmen regarding proposed legislative changes that would adversely affect your Medicaid status. The more involved you can keep those closest to you, the better able they'll be help you when you need it.

Note: My mom took things the hardest. Her concerns were double mine. You see, she was worried not only about JC, but about me, too.

A special nod to my mother in law who happens to be a retired physician, her experience and exposure to individuals with disabilities allowed her to take things in stride and help the rest of us to embrace an unknown future.

DAY 29: MEDICAL

"What Are Developmental Milestones?

The term milestones is derived from the word "stone marker", which is placed along the road to indicate distance traveled. To develop is to expand or realize the potentialities of; bring to fuller, greater, or better state. By tracking a child's developmental milestones, parents and physicians are able to monitor a child's learning, behavior, and development, and mark the child's progress along his/her developmental journey.

Development is commonly discussed in terms of domains of function. Gross motor skills refer to the use of large muscles of the body; fine motor skills refer to the use of small muscles of the hands; language refers to the comprehension (receptive language) and production (expressive language) of meaningful symbolic communication; and social functioning refers to emotional reactions to events and interactions with others. The range of developmental milestones in children with Down syndrome is wide, and may be impacted by medical issues (e.g., seizures, hearing loss). It is important for parents to know what is within the expected range, and to make sure that their child is progressing appropriately. For example, gross motor develops in an organized fashion from head to toe. Head control is the infant's first control task. Once a child gains sufficient control of shoulder and upper trunk, he is able to roll over. Subsequently, trunk control emerges to help with sitting. As voluntary control moves to the hips and legs, the child is capable of getting up on the hands and knees to crawl, cruise, and eventually walk independently.

Parents and therapists should be sure to recognize that the child is achieving the milestones correctly. For instance, a child should not walk on tiptoes when learning how to walk independently. It is important to communicate with your child's therapists and pediatrician to make sure that your child is achieving the milestones correctly and continues to make progress.

It is important for parents to know what is within the expected range, and to make sure that their child is pressing appropriately.

DAY 30: PARENT

"Your Baby"

So here we are at Day 30, and I've yet to mention anything about financial waivers, chromosomes, research materials, the "everyone's looking at me" syndrome, and so much more. And, we still haven't talked much about the baby. While you are adapting to your life as a mom with a child who has Down syndrome, busy reading, researching, learning (perhaps having a few break downs now and again), your baby is calmly waiting, docile and content. Down syndrome babies are the best babies a mother could ask for; yet, that doesn't mean they don't need us. In fact, they may need us more. They need us to be aware of what they are not doing. They may not cry to be changed. They may not cry to be swaddled, fed, or held. They may not wake up for nightly feedings. They may not be reaching out to grab your finger or to touch the world around them. Your inner detective needs to assess what your baby is missing, so that you can provide it.

Here a few things we did that seemed helpful. First, we made every effort to ensure JC was held a lot. This way he was able to explore new faces, materials, smells, and get a sense of the people and the world around him as he was carried. We also learned how to swaddle properly—swaddling helps an infant feel safe, all the while keeping their limbs secure in a natural position. Since JC had weak muscle tone, with his arms, legs, and head all wanting to move in different directions, he needed to be swaddled. We also closely monitored his food intake, weight, and bowel movements to ensure he was getting the nutrients he needed and was growing properly. Since he didn't fuss if hungry, we fed on a schedule, including setting an alarm to wake us for night feedings. And he wouldn't always cry when wet or soiled, so we proactively checked. Much of raising a child with Down syndrome means being proactive. No time like the present to start.

Many of you probably plan on going back to work. I did, but I had to find a day care that I thought would care for my son appropriately. I have learned that with day cares and schools alike, people will either have no clue, desire, or infrastructure to care for a child with special needs, or they will bend over backwards to become part of your community. It is this more than anything that guides my decisions. The facility doesn't have to be the newest or have the best technology, but the people dealing directly with my son and the supervisors who support them must embrace the vision of an inclusive environment. The ingredients that help to make a great day care setting are a desire to provide excellent care, a good vision, lots of love, and a bit of experience. If you have these elements in place, you can feel pretty sure you are in good hands.

Good Environment = Vision + Love + Desire + Experience

We were lucky to find a local church day care that was happy to have JC not only in their nursery but also in their pre-school as he grew. As mentioned, we did end up having to leave the facility a short three months later, because JC got pneumonia and needed to be removed from a day care environment, but those facilities exist and are good options.

Another option, which turned out to be our best choice and a real blessing to our family, is a creative nanny who specializes in special needs. Our nanny's structure, discipline, and creativity were priceless. She spent hours with our son repeating therapeutic plans from our therapists. She did much of the "work," allowing us to have the time we needed to be just parents.

In Summary: Medical

"Be Your Child's Advocate"

In my interactions with children with Down syndrome, I have observed many who overcame obstacles that should have held them back, and I was overwhelmed by the realization that everyone is valuable, important, and capable if encouraged and given the opportunity. With appropriate and ongoing interventional therapies and resources, your child will make progress. Your child will be able to do many things. He will have many strengths and areas of challenges as well, just like any other child. He will be able to learn to talk and to sing. He will be able to go to school and to learn to read and write. He will be able to tell you "No" when he does not want to do something. He will love you and make you smile and laugh. You will have many wonderful days and a few bad days as well, just like any parents.

All children have passions and goals and to see only the diagnosis of Down syndrome is to ignore the amazing possibilities that lie within that child. It is easy to define a person's abilities and limitations by a diagnosis; our challenge then is to inspire others who interact with your child (e.g., teachers, therapists, family members) to look for all possibilities in a child, regardless of the diagnosis, and provide ongoing guidance and encouragement to help each child achieve their maximum potential.

And don't forget to take a break and enjoy yourself! Being a new parent is a lot of work and can be stressful at times. This is a doctor's order-- allow your spouse or a family member you can trust to take the reins for a day, giving you time to relax and decompress. Your emotional state impacts both you and your newborn, so do yourself and your baby a wonderful favor and take a breather!

Your child will be able to do many things. She will have many strengths and areas of challenges as well, just like any other child. She will be able to learn to talk and to sing. She will be able to go to school and to learn to read and write. She will be able to tell you "No" when she does not want to do something. She will love you and make you smile and laugh.

In Summary: Parent

"Everyone Is Looking At Me"

In closing, I want to mention the "everyone is looking at me" syndrome that we tend to develop when we have a child with Down syndrome. I have found that it is true that people do sometimes look at you and I have categorized the reasons.

1) You have a baby and people look at people with babies. My second son got a lot of stares too.

2) Those who are looking hard, usually have something to share. I have met many folks that I thought were staring and learned that they had a brother, sister, grandchild, friend, or neighbor who has Down syndrome. They have learned to love these folks and are genuinely excited to see that you have a baby with Down syndrome

3) Children sometimes will stare because they are curious and not afraid to stare because they want to learn about your child.

It is the folks that do not stare, that avoid because they are uncomfortable or oblivious that I have found to be more the issue. It is when people do not understand that they are unable to make good decisions and tend to want to isolate you and your child from the community, schools, activities and the like.

My learning and closure to my segment of this book is to "LET THEM LOOK!" Invite folks to look! Invite folks into your wonderful world and educate and advocate! The more people know about our wonderful children and all there many capabilities, the better choices they will make and the better lives we will all lead. Together we are stronger!

For you it means that with your new life, there comes new responsibility. Of course, you now have responsibility for a child, but you also have responsibility to pave the way for that child. You are up for the task. We all are and it is not that hard. My advice is to let common sense and heart guide you on your journey. You will know what your child is capable of and the life that your child deserves. Once you have that vision, begin working with those in your community to create it. There are many of us on the same journey who share the same visions, so you will have lots of folks to help you, and you will make lots of friends along the way.

I look forward to the day when our paths may cross and that I may stare at your beautiful family. You will stare back at mine and as so many of us with children with Down syndrome we will feel a kinship, share a knowing smile, exchange numbers and feel comfort in knowing that there are others who also walk our path.

Suggested Readings

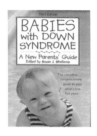

Babies with Down Syndrome - A New Parent's Guide
Susan J. Skallerup

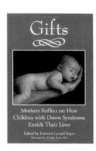

Gifts: Mothers Reflect on How Children with Down Syndrome Enrich Their Lives
Kathryn Lynard Soper

Road Map to Holland: How I Found My Way Through My Son's First Two Years With Down Syndrome
Jennifer Graf Groneberg

What's Inside You Is Inside Me, Too: My Chromosomes Make Me Unique
Deslie Webb Quinby and Jeannie Visootsak MD
Illustrated by Michael Johnson